McGraw-Hill Reading

WonderWorks

Unit 1
Decodable Reader

Mc
Graw
Hill
Education

Bothell, WA • Chicago, IL • Columbus, OH • New York, NY

Contents

by Emily Hansen
illustrated by Kate Flanagan

17

A Big Plan

by John Niles
illustrated by Olivia Cole

25

Is Rock Fun?

by Harold Kurtz
illustrated by Lynne Avril

33

We Can!

by Magali Rivera

We can go to  .

school

We can  .

paint

We can  .
read

We can play.

We can  .

eat

We can!

Jan Can Pack

by Allison Rivera
illustrated by Eva Vagreti

Jan packs.

Jan has a cap.

What can Jan pack?

Jan packs a bag.

Jan packs a pad.

Jan packs for **school**!
Dad **does** **not**.

Sit Down Kids!

by Emily Hansen
illustrated by Kate Flanagan

Sid sits.

Liz sits. Tim sits.

Kids go quick!

Sid sits **down**.
Liz sits down.

Sid is **up**.

Liz is up. Quick!

Will Sid sit?
Will Liz sit?

Liz is **out**.
Sid is **very** quick.

A Big Plan

by John Niles
illustrated by Olivia Cole

Jill has a big plan.

Jill will **pull** a sack down.

Jill will clip, clip rag bits.

A flag will **be** **good**.

Jill clips and slips rag bits.

Come, see a big pig flag!

Is Rock Fun?

by Harold Kurtz
illustrated by Lynne Avril

Bam, bam, bam.
Bob can **make** rock.

Rat-a-tat.
Bob taps on.

They do not like rock.

Dad has a big box.
Mom is glad.

Mom has a box, **too**.
Dad is glad.

They can block it.
Rock is **fun**!

Unit 1

Decoding skills taught to date:

Phonics: Short *a*; Short *i*; *l*-Blends; Short *o*

Structural Analysis: Inflectional Ending -*s* (plurals, verbs); Double Final Consonants; Alphabetical Order